INAUGURAL   EXHIBITION

AMON CARTER MUSEUM OF WESTERN ART

Selected Works

Frederic Remington   and   Charles Marion Russell

Fort Worth, Texas   •   1961   •   January 21

The inheritance of a legacy imposes many responsibilities and duties. Specifically, faithfulness and loyalty to a legacy of the dreams and hopes of a man of vision demand, above all, humility and dedication to ideals of staggering proportions.

As heirs to the spirit and the keeping of the trust of his ideals, we, the directors of the Amon G. Carter Foundation present this Museum of Western Art to the "education, interest and pleasure of all the citizens of this great area, 'Where the West Begins'" that it may forever enlighten us, and be our companion to remind us of the great heritage which we must nourish to keep alive.

Ruth Carter Johnson

for the Foundation

The Amon Carter Museum is indebted to the following people for their inestimable assistance in connection with the Museum and the Exhibition: Mr. Frank R. Little, Remington Art Memorial Museum, Ogdensburg, New York; Miss Helen L. Card, Latendorf Book Shop, New York; Mr. F. G. Renner, Washington, D. C.; Mr. Harold McCracken, Gertrude Vanderbilt Whitney Gallery of Western Art, Cody, Wyoming; Mr. Michael Kennedy, Historical Society of Montana, Helena, Montana; Mr. William H. Bertsche, Jr., C. M. Russell Gallery, Great Falls, Montana; Mr. James Taylor Forrest, Gilcrease Foundation, Tulsa, Oklahoma, and Mr. Rene d'Harnoncourt, Museum of Modern Art, New York.

AMON G. CARTER (1879-1955)

A painting is, of course, the production of an artist. Good paintings are produced by artists able to understand the mood of a time and the mood of the people there, able to record and preserve these historical impressions for the knowledge and enjoyment of those to follow, those who did not have the privilege of being there. Paintings are among the most valuable of our heritages, able to record and interpret history even better than the printed page.

Paintings should be acquired, owned and preserved by those who have a deep affection for them. You do not have an affection for a painting unless you understand its significance. It has to bring back some pleasant memory, it has to rekindle some earlier ambition or it has to tell about a time and a people dear to you.

Amon G. Carter understood paintings by Charles M. Russell and Frederic Remington because their subject was the frontier and their story was about the courage of the pioneer, about the men and women who had curiosity about what was on the other side of the horizon and the fortitude to go there and be acquainted with it. It was this kind of people who made the colorful days of the Old West, of Texas and of Fort Worth.

Amon G. Carter knew the pioneering days and he knew the pioneers. Why? Because that was his time and these were his people—he was one of them. Amon admired intellectual curiosity, he admired determination and he admired courage. And all of these admirable traits he had in abundance. When Amon looked at one of these glorious paintings he said to himself: "There I would like to have been."

Amon G. Carter was born and reared in a frontier community. He acquired there the habits which later brought success to his business life. He also acquired and thereafter maintained a spirit of generosity. He wanted others to do well, he wanted to share with others the opportunities which come to able men.

This museum and these paintings are here for a specific reason and purpose, because Amon G. Carter loved the days of the pioneer and he wanted to give you an opportunity to form an affection for these sturdy men and women of the earlier days. This museum and its paintings are a continuing memorial to a fine and generous man, Amon G. Carter.

C. R. Smith

SITE PLAN

If it is true that sometimes civilizations are remembered by their buildings—and what else do we know of the people who built the Mexican pyramids or even the Egyptian—today's buildings to be remembered may very well be its museums. Today we do not build—for whatever reasons—cathedrals and temples. Business and industry are the great patrons of the structural arts.

But in the long view the profit motive and the management calculus are insufficient to build monuments enough for this century. May not the twenty-first century look at our skyscrapers and judge them as we judge, at the very best, the anonymous towers of San Gimignano? May not future historians ask where our Bramante Churches and our Palladian Palaces are? Leaving aside the question of whether we have today architects as good as Bramante and Palladio, we certainly have no churches and no palaces to equal theirs. But the Museum is a new concept in building history. It is barely 150 years in the three thousand or so years of western architecture since the first deliberately monumental museums were built, and now this year a museum has become the most important—and the most talked of monument of the year: The Guggenheim Museum in New York by the late Frank Lloyd Wright.

Museums, not city halls, palaces, state capitols, movie houses, opera houses are the buildings people look to today. They play a new symbolic part in the life of our cities. Attendance goes up. People spend the day in their restaurants, their lecture rooms, their gardens, their movie theaters. Psychologists and sociologists may explain to us this phenomenon, but the duty of the architects, of the patrons of the city, is clear. We must build handsome museums.

I can say nothing of the contents. It is true there must be art and Art inside the buildings, but my particular part of the job is to make the Museum building "art," in order better to view the Art inside, as well as to give pleasure of a public and communal nature.

The problem of the Amon Carter Museum of Western Art is very special. Not only is the building to house art and be a public monument, but beyond that to be a memorial to an extraordinary man. The task is formidable.

The traditional academic International Style modern architecture seemed inadequate to express the memorial function of the building. Steel, glass and aluminum, seemed

FACADE

VIEW FROM INTERIOR (under construction)

unworthy materials for a civic monument. Movable fibre-board partitions seemed too miserable a wall material for fine paintings. The fine shell stone of Texas, on the contrary, lent itself admirably to a formal building, located in Texas. The site, a noble slope overlooking the city's center, led naturally to a portico design.

The five segmental arches on tapered columns form an open porch overlooking terraced areas, much as a Greek stoa or Renaissance loggia overlooked Mediterranean plazas, a shaded place looking on a sunny openness. Behind the colonnade, a glass wall separates the art from the city, the cool from the warm, the peaceful from the active, the still from the windy.

The Great Hall, two stories high and the full length of the building, is not only space for showing, but a Memorial Hall, into which the art galleries proper debouch. Five rooms, the proper size for installing pictures by Remington and Russell are each entered by a double doorway from the Great Hall.

Above the picture galleries are five more rooms, each with a balcony view on the Great Hall. The offices are in this upper floor, storage and more offices in the basement. Beyond the regular functioning of the building, the Amon Carter Museum of Western Art will, it is hoped, satisfy the function of decorating the city of Fort Worth and honoring the memory of Amon Carter.

Philip Johnson

BIOGRAPHY OF FREDERIC REMINGTON   (1861-1909)

1861 Frederic Remington born October 1, Canton, New York, son of Seth Pierrepont and Clara Remington

1876 Sent to Highland Military Academy, Worcester, Massachusetts

1878-1880 Studied at Yale School of Fine Arts

1880 Made trip West, worked as cowboy, scout, sheep and mule rancher

1882 First sketch appeared in *Harper's Weekly:* "Cowboys of Arizona Aroused by a Scout"

1884 Sold ranch in Kansas and traveled to the Southwest. Later returned to Kansas City where he began his serious art career. On October 1 of this year Remington married Eva Adele Caten of Gloversville, New York

1885 Once more traveled to the Southwest prospecting. Later made a trip to New York with sketches for sale and studied briefly at the Art Students League

1886 Appearance of first picture to carry Remington's name alone, the beginning of his career as an illustrator. Also in this year the first book with illustrations by Remington, *Mexico of Today* by Solomon Buckley Griffin, was published

1887 Painting, "The Flag of Truce in the Indian Wars," was hung in the annual exhibition of the American Watercolor Society. "Courier's Nap on the Trail" hung in the annual exhibition of the National Academy of Design

1888 Won the Clarke and the Hallgarten prizes at the annual exhibition of the National Academy of Design

1889 Received a Silver Medal at the Paris Exhibition

1890 Accompanied General Miles' expedition into the Badlands to put down Sioux uprising

1891 Made an associate of the National Academy of Design

1892 Made trip abroad to Europe, Russia and North Africa, with Poultney Bigelow

1893 First exhibit and sale of pictures in New York

1898 Remington accompanied Richard Harding Davis to Cuba for the Hearst Syndicate and *Harper's Magazine*

1903 Began work for *Collier's* as an artist under a contract which left him free to choose his own subjects

1904 Plaster replica of bronze sculpture "Coming Through the Rye," exhibited at the St. Louis World Fair

1905 March 18 issue of *Collier's Weekly* devoted to Remington's works

1909 Purchased farm near Ridgefield, Connecticut where he died after an operation for appendicitis on December 26 of the same year

1. CAVALRY IN AN ARIZONA SANDSTORM.
Date: c. 1889, date of first reproduction.
Signed lower right: Remington.
Medium: Oil, black and white, on canvas.
Size: 22″ x 35″.
Exhibited: Fort Worth Art Association Gallery, Fort Worth Public Library, 1950.
Reproduced: *Harper's Weekly*, September 14, 1889.

2. A DASH FOR TIMBER.

Date: 1889, dated.

Signed lower left: Frederic Remington '89.

Medium: Oil on canvas.

Size: 48″ x 84″.

Ex-collection: Washington University, St. Louis, Missouri.

Exhibited: National Academy Autumn Exhibition, 1889. Dallas Museum of Fine Arts, 1936.

Reproduced: *Frederic Remington—Artist of the Old West*, Harold McCracken. *Lure of the Frontier*, Ralph Henry Gabriel. *The High Trail*, E. D. Starbuck. *The American Heritage Book of the Pioneer Spirit. The Fireside Book of Guns*, Larry Koller. *Art Digest*, June, 1936. *Art Digest*, April, 1945. *Time*, May 14, 1945. *Art News*, June, 1946. *Country Gentleman*, September, 1947. *Minneapolis Star-Tribune*, January 4, 1948. Issued as an art print by Elson Art Publications Company, Incorporated.

3. THE DRUM CORPS ON PARADE.
Date: c. 1889, date of first reproduction.
Signed lower left: Frederic Remington, City of Mexico.
Medium: Oil on wood.
Size: 18″ x 28″.
Ex-collection: James Cromwell, former ambassador to Canada.
Exhibited: Fort Worth Art Association Gallery, Fort Worth Public Library, 1950.
Reproduced: *Harper's Monthly,* November, 1889. *Armies of Today,* Thomas Janvier.

4. AN INDIAN TRAPPER.

Date: 1889, dated.

Signed lower left: Frederic Remington '89.

Medium: Oil on canvas.

Size: 49¼″ x 34″.

Reproduced: *Harper's Monthly*, May, 1890. *Riders of Many Lands*, Theodore Ayrault
Dodge. *Harper's Weekly*, January, 1910. *The Book of the American
Indian*, Hamlin Garland. *True, the Man's Magazine*, May, 1954.

5. CANADIAN MOUNTED POLICE ON A WINTER EXPEDITION.
Date: c. 1890, date of first reproduction.
Signed lower right: Frederic Remington.
Medium: Oil, black and white, on canvas.
Size: 20″ x 32″.
Ex-collection: The Honorable Joseph S. Frelinghuysen, senator from New Jersey.
Exhibited: Fort Worth Art Association Gallery, Fort Worth Public Library, 1950.
Reproduced: *Harper's Weekly,* March 22, 1890.

6. THE SCOUT'S PAUSE, or, THE VAQUERO.
Date: c. 1890, date of first reproduction.
Signed lower right: Frederic Remington.
Medium: Oil, black and white, on canvas.
Size: 28½″ x 18¼″.
Ex-collection: The Honorable Joseph S. Frelinghuysen, senator from New Jersey.
Exhibited: Fort Worth Art Association Gallery, Fort Worth Public Library, 1950.
Reproduced: *Harper's Monthly,* October, 1890. *South American Republics,* Theodore Child.

7. MULE TRAIN.
Date: c. 1890-1891, the year Remington campaigned with the United States Cavalry.
Signed lower right: Frederic Remington.
Medium: Pen and ink on paper.
Size: 6½″ x 22½″.
Ex-collection: James Cromwell, former ambassador to Canada.
Exhibited: Fort Worth Art Association Gallery, Fort Worth Public Library, 1950.

8. THE SCOUT'S REPORT AT BREAKFAST ON THE PLAINS.
Date: c. 1890-1891, year Remington campaigned with United States Cavalry.
Signed lower left: Frederic Remington.
Medium: Oil on canvas.
Size: 22″ x 32½″.
Ex-collection: The Honorable Joseph S. Frelinghuysen, senator from New Jersey.
Exhibited: The Fort Worth Art Association Gallery, Fort Worth Public Library, 1950.

9. THE BARRACKS.
Date: c. 1892, date of Remington's trip to North Africa.
Signed lower right: Frederic Remington.
Medium: Oil on canvas.
Size: 24″ x 20″.
Exhibited: Fort Worth Art Association Gallery, Fort Worth Public Library, 1950.

10. A REVOLVER CHARGE.
Date: c. 1892, date of Remington's trip to North Africa.
Signed lower left: Frederic Remington, Algiers.
Medium: Oil on canvas.
Size: 35¾″ x 60″.
Ex-collection: Mrs. Elmer E. Smathers, New York.
Exhibited: Holland Galleries, Babcock Galleries, M. Knoedler and Company, New York.
Reproduced: *Harper's Monthly,* December, 1894.

11. HORSE'S HEAD. (Illustrated on dust jacket).
Date: c. 1895.
Signed lower right: Frederic Remington.
Medium: Oil on canvas.
Size: 24¾″ x 20″.

12. MORGAN'S MEN HOLDING UP THE FORAGE TRAIN.
Date: c. 1895, date of first reproduction.
Signed lower left: Frederic Remington.
Medium: Black and white wash on board.
Size: 21¾" x 29⅝".
Ex-collection: The Honorable Joseph S. Frelinghuysen, senator from New Jersey.
Exhibited: Fort Worth Art Association Gallery, Fort Worth Public Library, 1950.
Reproduced: *Cosmopolitan Magazine,* March, 1895.

13. THE TORTOISE AND THE HARE.
Date: 1900, dated.
Signed lower left: Frederic Remington copyright 1900.
Medium: Oil, black and white, on canvas.
Size: 27¼" x 40¼".
Ex-collection: James Cromwell, former ambassador to Canada.
Exhibited: Fort Worth Art Association Gallery, Fort Worth Public Library, 1950.
Reproduced: *Done in the Open.* Drawings by Frederic Remington with an introduction by Owen Wister.

14. THE SMUGGLERS.
Date: c. 1901, date of first reproduction.
Signed lower right: Frederic Remington.
Medium: Oil, black and white, on canvas.
Size: 40⅜" x 27¼".
Ex-collection: James Cromwell, former ambassador to Canada.
Exhibited: Fort Worth Art Association Gallery, Fort Worth Public Library, 1950.
Reproduced: *Collier's Weekly,* October 26, 1901. *Done in the Open.* Drawings by Frederic Remington with an introduction by Owen Wister.

15. THE COWBOY.
Date: c. 1902, date of first reproduction.
Signed lower right: Frederic Remington.
Medium: Oil on canvas.
Size: 40¼" x 27".
Ex-collection: John Howard, Ogdensburg, New York; a personal friend of Remington, who acquired the painting from the artist. John Howard, Jr., William J. Healey.
Exhibited: Remington Museum, Ogdensburg, New York.
Reproduced: *Scribner's Magazine,* October, 1902. Issued as a colored lithograph by Charles Scribner's Sons in the series *Western Types. Scribner's Magazine,* January, 1937. *Spur Magazine,* 1938. *Life,* September 14, 1942. *Frederic Remington, A Painter of American Life,* Robert Isaacson. *Frederic Remington—Artist of the Old West,* Harold McCracken. *Life in America,* Marshall B. Davidson. *The American Muse,* published by the Viking Press.

16. THE OLD STAGE COACH OF THE PLAINS.

Date: c. 1902, date of first reproduction.

Signed lower right: Frederic Remington.

Medium: Oil on canvas.

Size: 40″ x 27″.

Ex-collection: George P. Messervy, New York: Mrs. C. T. Jeffrey.

Exhibited: Fort Worth Art Association Gallery, Fort Worth Public Library, 1950.

Reproduced: Cover, *The Century Magazine,* January, 1902. Also reproduced on poster advertising the January 1902 issue of *The Century Magazine.* Reproduced as a color print.

17. THROW UP YOUR HANDS.

Date: c. 1902, date of first reproduction.

Signed lower right: Frederic Remington.

Medium: Oil, black and white, on canvas.

Size: 27¼″ x 40½″.

Ex-collection: James Cromwell, former Ambassador to Canada.

Exhibited: Fort Worth Art Association Gallery, Fort Worth Public Library, 1950.

Reproduced: *Collier's Weekly,* May 17, 1902. *Ranson's Folly,* Richard Harding Davis.

18. HIS FIRST LESSON.

Date: 1903, dated.

Signed lower right: copyright 1903 by Frederic Remington.

Medium: Oil on canvas.

Size: 27″ x 40½″.

Ex-collection: Governor E. W. Marland of Oklahoma. W. L. Moody, III, Galveston, Texas.

Exhibited: Noe Art Galleries, 1903. Fine Arts Exposition, Ehrich-Newhouse Galleries, 1934. Fort Worth Art Association Gallery, Fort Worth Public Library, 1950.

Reproduced: *Collier's Weekly*, September 26, 1903. *New York American*, December 27, 1909. *New York Sun*, December 1, 1934. *Frederic Remington— Artist of the Old West,* Harold McCracken. Issued as an art print by P. F. Collier and Sons, American Federation of Arts, and Dodge Publishing Company.

19. THE RECONNAISSANCE.
Date: 1903, dated.
Signed lower right: Frederic Remington copyright 1903.
Medium: Oil on canvas.
Size: 27″ x 40″.
Reproduced: *Collier's Weekly,* April 8, 1905.

20. PONY TRACKS ON THE BUFFALO TRAIL.

Date: c. 1904, date of first reproduction.

Signed lower right: Frederic Remington.

Medium: Oil on canvas.

Size: 30″ x 51¼″.

Reproduced: *Collier's Weekly*, October 8, 1904. Reproduced as a color print by P. F.
          Collier and Sons, and by Dodge Publishing Company.

21. RIDDEN DOWN.
Date: 1905, copyright date.
Signed lower left: Frederic Remington.
Medium: Oil on canvas.
Size: 30″ x 51½″.
Reproduced: *True, the Man's Magazine,* May, 1954.

22. THE LONGHORN CATTLE SIGN.
Date: 1908, dated.
Signed lower right: Frederic Remington 1908.
Medium: Oil on canvas.
Size: 27″ x 40″.
Ex-collection: J. B. Cobb, who bought the painting from Remington.
Exhibited: Knoedler's Galleries, New York, 1908.
Reproduced: *Collier's Weekly,* May 6, 1911. Reproduced as a color print by Dodge
 Publishing Company and the Art Extension Press, Incorporated.

23. THE SMOKE SIGNAL.
Date: c. 1909.
Signed lower left: Frederic Remington.
Medium: Oil on canvas.
Size: 30" x 48".
Reproduced: *The Smoke Signal*, Harold McCracken.

24. BRONCO BUSTER.

Date: 1895, copyright date.

Signed: Copyright by Frederic Remington.

Size: 32½″.

Cast by: Roman Bronze Works, New York.

Number of cast: 5.

Number of casts made: Only a few of this large size were cast, possibly 12 to 15, according to Harold McCracken and Mr. Bertelli, founder of the Roman Bronze Works, who supervised the casting of Remington's bronzes.

Ex-collection: W. W. Cohen, New York. Sickles Collection, Chicago.

25.   THE FALLEN RIDER (THE WICKED PONY).
Date: 1898, copyright date.
Signed: Frederic Remington.
Size: 22″.
Cast by: Henry Bonnard Company, New York.
Number of cast: 4.

26.   THE CHEYENNE (THE CHEYENNE WARRIOR).
Date: 1901, copyright date.
Signed: Copyright by Frederic Remington.
Size: 24″.
Cast by: Roman Bronze Works, New York.
Ex-collection: Richard M. Nesbitt, New York.

27.   COMING THROUGH THE RYE.

Date: 1902, copyright date.

Signed: Frederic Remington.

Size: 20″.

Cast by: Roman Bronze Works, New York.

Number of cast: 7.

Ex-collection: C. R. Smith, New York.

Exhibited: Fort Worth Art Association Gallery, Fort Worth Public Library, 1950.

28.   THE TRAPPER (THE MOUNTAIN MAN).

Date: 1903, copyright date.

Signed: Copyright by Frederic Remington.

Size: 28″.

Cast by: Roman Bronze Works, New York.

Ex-collection: Richard M. Nesbitt, New York.

29. THE SERGEANT.
Date: 1904, copyright date.
Signed: Frederic Remington. Copyright by Frederic Remington.
Size: 11″.
Cast by: Roman Bronze Works, New York.

30. RATTLESNAKE IN THE PATH.
Date: 1905, copyright date.
Signed: Copyright Frederic Remington.
Size: 20".
Cast by: Roman Bronze Works, New York.
Ex-collection: C. R. Smith, New York.

31. THE COWBOY (THE OUTLAW).
Date: 1906, copyright date.
Signed: Frederic Remington.
Size: 23".
Cast by: Roman Bronze Works, New York.
Number of cast: 27.
Ex-collection: Richard M. Nesbitt, New York.

32. THE STAMPEDE. (Illustrated above)
Date: 1909, copyright date.
Signed: Copyright Frederic Remington.
Size: 23".
Cast by: Roman Bronze Works, New York.
Number of cast: 6.
Number of casts made: 10.

33. TROOPER OF THE PLAINS, 1868.
Date: 1909, copyright date.
Signed: Copyright Frederic Remington.
Size: 28".
Cast by: Roman Bronze Works, New York.
Number of cast: 11.
Ex-collection: William B. Leeds, New York. John Sinnot.

BIOGRAPHY OF CHARLES MARION RUSSELL (1864-1926)

1864 Charles Marion Russell born March 19, St. Louis, Missouri

1879 Sent to Burlington Military Academy, Burlington, New Jersey

1880 Made first trip west to Montana where he worked as a sheep rancher, trapper, and cowboy for more than ten years

1882 After a short visit home Russell decided to return to Montana. He was accompanied by a young cousin who died after reaching Helena. Russell continued on to the Judith Basin of Montana, where he took the first of his many jobs as a cowboy for various outfits in Montana

1887 Sketch "Waiting for a Chinook" shown in Helena and reproduced as a postcard. Russell's fame as an artist was spread and he received offers of training in the East or in Europe

1888 Lived with the Blood Indians in Canada. Gathered material for his many sketches of Indian life. Painting "Caught in the Act" with explanatory text by the artist reproduced in *Harper's Weekly*

1889 Russell returned to Judith Basin and cowboy life. May 18 issue of *Leslie's Illustrated Newspaper* carried an article and a full page of drawings by Russell

1890 *Studies of Western Life,* portfolio of scenes of cowboys and Indians by Russell with text by Granville Stuart published

1893 Abandoned the life of the professional cowboy and settled down to a full-time pursuit of artist's career

1896 Married Nancy Cooper, September 9, in Cascade, Montana

1897 April issue of *Recreation* published Russell's first article "Early Days on the Buffalo Range." In this year, Russell and his wife moved to Great Falls, Montana

1898 First bronze casting, a medallion with an Indian head, made at Roman Bronze Works, New York

1903 "Pirate of the Plains" and other pictures accepted for hanging in the Fine Arts Building at St. Louis World's Fair. In this year Russell held his first showing of paintings in New York City, and the first of his many small bronze statues, "Smoking Up" was cast

1904-1905 Three miniature bronze groups "Buffalo Hunt," "Counting Coup," and "Scalp Dance" exhibited at Tiffany's

1911 Russell commissioned to do mural at rear of speaker's desk in the Montana House of Representatives, his largest picture. In this year, the edition of *The Virginian* by Owen Wister with illustrations by Russell was published

1914 Exhibition of paintings held at Dore Galleries in London, England. The following year many exhibitions of Russell paintings were held at various galleries throughout the United States

1921 *Rawhide Rawlins,* collection of cowboy stories by Russell, published

1925 Received honorary degree of LLD from the University of Montana

1926 On October 24, Charles Marion Russell died of a heart attack in Great Falls, Montana

34.   UTICA PICTURE.

Date: c. 1885.

Signed lower right: CMR intertwined (near skull of buffalo)

Medium: Oil on canvas.

Size: 23⅜″ x 47½″.

Ex-collection: Sid Willis, The Mint Bar, Great Falls, Montana.

Exhibited: M. Knoedler and Company, New York, 1952. Pioneer Palace, Fort Worth, Texas, 1952.

Reproduced: *Seventh Report of the Bureau of Agriculture, Labor and Industry of Montana, 1900. Charles M. Russell Book*, Harold McCracken. *Montana: The Magazine of Western History*. Autumn, 1958.

35. WILD MEAT FOR WILD MEN.
Date: 1890, dated.
Signed lower left: CM Russell 1890 (Skull).
Medium: Oil on canvas.
Size: 20″ x 36″.
Exhibited: Fort Worth Art Association Gallery, Fort Worth Public Library, 1950.

36. BRINGING HOME THE GAME.

Date: 1896, dated.

Signed lower left: CM Russell (Skull) 1896.

Medium: Oil on canvas.

Size: 36½″ x 24″.

Ex-collection: Sid Willis, The Mint Bar, Great Falls, Montana.

Exhibited: M. Knoedler and Company, New York, 1952. Pioneer Palace, Fort Worth, Texas, 1952.

Reproduced: *Mint Souvenir Catalog*, 1928. *Glimpse of Great Falls, Montana*.

37. HUNTSMAN AND DOGS.
Date: 1898, dated.
Signed lower left: CM Russell (Skull) 1898.
Medium: Watercolor on paper mounted on board.
Size: 10″ x 14½″.
Ex-collection: Colonel William Boyce Thompson, James Richard Thompson, and James
        Arthur Thompson.

38. MOOSE HUNT.
Date: 1898, dated.
Signed lower left: CM Russell (Skull) 1898.
Medium: Watercolor on paper.
Size: 13½″ x 17¼″.
Ex-collection: Sid Willis, The Mint Bar, Great Falls, Montana.
Exhibited: M. Knoedler and Company, New York, 1952. Pioneer Palace, Fort Worth,
        Texas, 1952.

39. THE HOLDUP.

Date: 1899, dated.

Signed lower left: CM Russell (Skull) 1899.

Medium: Oil on canvas.

Size: 30″ x 48″.

Ex-collection: Sid Willis, The Mint Bar, Great Falls, Montana.

Exhibited: M. Knoedler and Company, New York, 1952. Pioneer Palace, Fort Worth,
Texas, 1952.

Reproduced: *Colorprint*, William T. Ridgley, 1899. *Mint Souvenir Catalog*, 1928.
Western Prose and Poetry, Rufus A. Coleman, editor. *The Charles M.
Russell Book*, Harold McCracken. *Montana: The Magazine of Western
History*, Autumn 1957.

40. NATTUCE.

Date: 1903, dated.

Signed lower left: CM Russell 1903 (Skull).

Medium: Watercolor on paper.

Size: 12″ x 6¼″.

Ex-Collection: Sid Willis, The Mint Bar, Great Falls, Montana.

Exhibited: M. Knoedler and Company, New York, 1952. Pioneer Palace, Fort Worth,
Texas, 1952.

41. ROPING THE COYOTE.

Date: 1904, dated.

Signed lower left: CM Russell (Skull) 1904.

Medium: Oil on canvas.

Size: 24½″ x 29½″.

Ex-Collection: John A. Sleicher, Miss Mary Sleicher, Albany, New York.

42. THE DANGEROUS MOMENT.
Date: c. 1903.
Signed lower left: CM Russell (Skull).
Medium: Black and white wash on board.
Size: 24″ x 16″.
Ex-Collection: John A. Sleicher, Miss Mary Sleicher, Albany, New York.

43. THE RUSTLERS.
Date: 1904, dated.
Signed lower left: CM Russell (Skull) 1904.
Medium: Black and white watercolor on board.
Size: 25¾″ x 19⅛″.
Ex-Collection: John A. Sleicher, Miss Mary Sleicher, Albany, New York.
Reproduced: Cover, *Leslie's Weekly,* April 21, 1904.

44. LEWIS AND CLARK EXPEDITION ON THE LOWER COLUMBIA
     RIVER
Date: 1905, dated.
Signed lower left: CM Russell (Skull) 1905 copyright.
Medium: Watercolor on board.
Size: 18½″ x 23½″.
Ex-Collection: Copley Amory, Boston, Massachusetts.

45. THE BUFFALO HUNT.
Date: c. 1919.
Signed lower left: CM Russell (Skull) ©.
Medium: Oil on canvas.
Size: 30″ x 48″.
Ex-Collection: H. Edward Manville.
Exhibited: Fort Worth Art Association Gallery, Fort Worth Public Library, 1950.

46.   THREE WISE MEN.

Date: 1920, dated.

Signed lower left: CM Russell (Skull) 1920.

Medium: Watercolor on cardboard.

Size: 23½″ x 40″.

Ex-Collection: James W. Bollinger.

Reproduced: *Antiques,* December 1952.

47.   WHERE THE BEST OF RIDERS QUIT.

Date: 1925, copyright date.

Signed: CM Russell (Skull).

Size: 14½″.

Cast by: California Art Bronze Foundry, Los Angeles.

Number of casts made: 17.

48. MEAT FOR WILD MEN.
Date: 1925, copyright date.
Signed: CM Russell (Skull).
Size: 11¼″.
Cast by: Roman Bronze Works, New York.
Number of casts made: 4.

49. WILL ROGERS.
Date: 1928, copyright date.
Signed: CM Russell.
Size: 14½″.
Cast by: Nelli Art Bronze Works, Los Angeles.
Number of casts made: 20.
Ex-Collection: C. R. Smith, New York.
Exhibited: Fort Worth Art Association Gallery, Fort Worth Public Library, 1950.

SMALL BRONZES BY CHARLES MARION RUSSELL

The numbers refer to the Foundation's cataloguing.

2. BUFFALO HUNT. 10¼".

3. THE BRONCO BUSTER. 18".

4. BUCKER AND BUCKEROO. 15½".

5. SMOKING UP. 12½".

6. COUNTING COUP. 11½".

7. DOUGLAS FAIRBANKS. 11".

8. JIM BRIDGER. 14½".

10. THE HORSE WRANGLER. 14".

12. THE RANGE FATHER. 5½".

13. THE BLUFFERS. 7½".

14. PAINTING THE TOWN. 13½".

15. SMOKING TO THE SPIRIT OF THE BUFFALO. 4".

16. THE SPIRIT OF WINTER. 10".

17. A WATCHER OF THE PLAINS. 11".

18. TO NOSES THAT READ—A SMELL THAT SPELLS MAN. 5¾".

19. THE LAST LAUGH. 4½".

20. COMBAT. 6¾".

21. NATURE'S CATTLE. 7".

22. ENEMY TRACKS. 12".

23. BLACKFOOT WAR DANCE. 13½".

24. BUFFALO RUBBING ROCK. 5".

27. AN ENEMY THAT WARNS. 5".

28. OH, MOTHER, WHAT IS IT? 4".

29. SECRETS OF THE NIGHT. 13".

30. THE BUG HUNTERS. 6".

31. MOUNTAIN SHEEP. 8½".

32. THE BUFFALO FAMILY. 7".

33. BUFFALO. 5¼".

34. SLEEPING THUNDER. 7¼".

35. INDIAN MAIDEN. 7".

35. BEAR. 4¼".

37. SLEEPING CAT. 1½".

38. SEATED WOLF. 4".

39. THE TEXAS STEER. 4".

40. THE SCALP DANCER. 6½″.

41. THE FRIVOLOUS CUBS. 6¾″.

42. WAR CHIEF. 10½″.

43. THE SNAKE PRIEST. 4½″.

44. WOLF WITH BONE. 6″.

45. MEDICINE WHIP. 10″.

46. WEAPONS OF THE WEAK. 6″.

47. THE ROBE FLESHER. 5¼″.

48. A HAPPY FIND. 4½″.

49. THE MEDICINE MAN. 7″.

50. NAVAJO. 5″.

51. BEAR. 2¾″.

52. INDIAN FAMILY. 5½″.

53. BUFFALO LYING DOWN. 4″.

54. THE BEAR AND THE JUG. 5½″.

55. INDIAN FAMILY. 5″.

SELECTED BIBLIOGRAPHY

McCRACKEN, HAROLD, *Frederic Remington: Artist of the Old West*. Philadelphia: J. B. Lippincott Company: 1947.

McCRACKEN, HAROLD, *Frederic Remington Memorial Collection*. Privately printed for the Remington Art Memorial. Ogdensburg, New York, by The Knoedler Galleries, New York: 1954.

McCRACKEN, HAROLD, *Portrait of the Old West*. New York: McGraw-Hill Book Company, Inc.: 1952.

ADAMS, RAMON F. AND HOMER E. BRITZMAN, *Charles M. Russell, the Cowboy Artist: A Biography*. Pasadena, California: Trail's End Publishing Co., Inc.: 1948.

McCRACKEN, HAROLD, *The Charles M. Russell Book*. Garden City, N. Y.: Doubleday & Company, Inc.: 1957.

McCRACKEN, HAROLD, *Portrait of the Old West*. New York: McGraw-Hill Book Company, Inc.: 1952.

RUSSELL, AUSTIN, *C. M. R.: Charles M. Russell, Cowboy Artist*. New York: Twayne Publishers: 1957.

TEN THOUSAND COPIES OF THIS CATALOGUE PUBLISHED JANUARY, 1961